5.95

RICHARD CLAYDERMAN

GW00385412

SONGS OF LOVE

Wise Publications
London/New York/Sydney/Cologne

Exclusive distributors:
Music Sales Limited
8/9 Frith Street,
London W1V 5TZ,
England.

Music Sales Pty Limited
120 Rothschild Avenue,
Rosebery, NSW 2018,
Australia.

This book © Copyright 1988 by
Wise Publications
UK ISBN 0.7119.1481.8
Order No.AM71028

Designed by Sands Straker Studios Limited
Arranged by Frank Booth

Music Sales' complete catalogue lists thousands of titles and is free
from your local music book shop, or direct from Music Sales Limited.
Please send £1 in stamps for postage to
Music Sales Limited, 8/9 Frith Street, London W1V 5TZ.

Printed in the United Kingdom by
St. Edmundsbury Press, Bury St. Edmunds, Suffolk.

ALWAYS THERE/ ANYONE CAN FALL IN LOVE

Music by Simon May & Leslie Osborne
Words by Don Black

NIKITA

Music by Elton John
Words by Bernie Taupin

To Coda ⊕

DO YOU KNOW WHERE YOU'RE GOING TO?

Words by Gerry Goffin
Music by Michael Masser

THE LADY IN RED/

Words & Music by Chris De Burgh

TAKE MY BREATH AWAY

Words by Tom Whitlock Music by Giorgio Moroder

THEME FROM 'THE BRETTS'

By David Cullen & David Mackay

I KNOW HIM SO WELL

Words & Music by Benny Andersson, Tim Rice & Bjorn Ulvaeus

YOU ARE MY WORLD

Words & Music by Jimmy Sommerville & Richard Coles

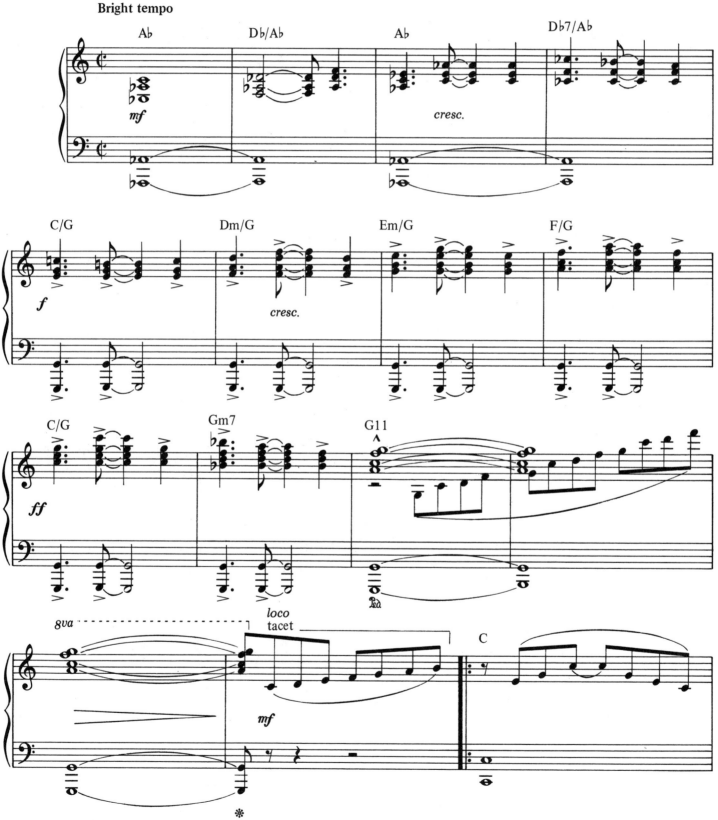

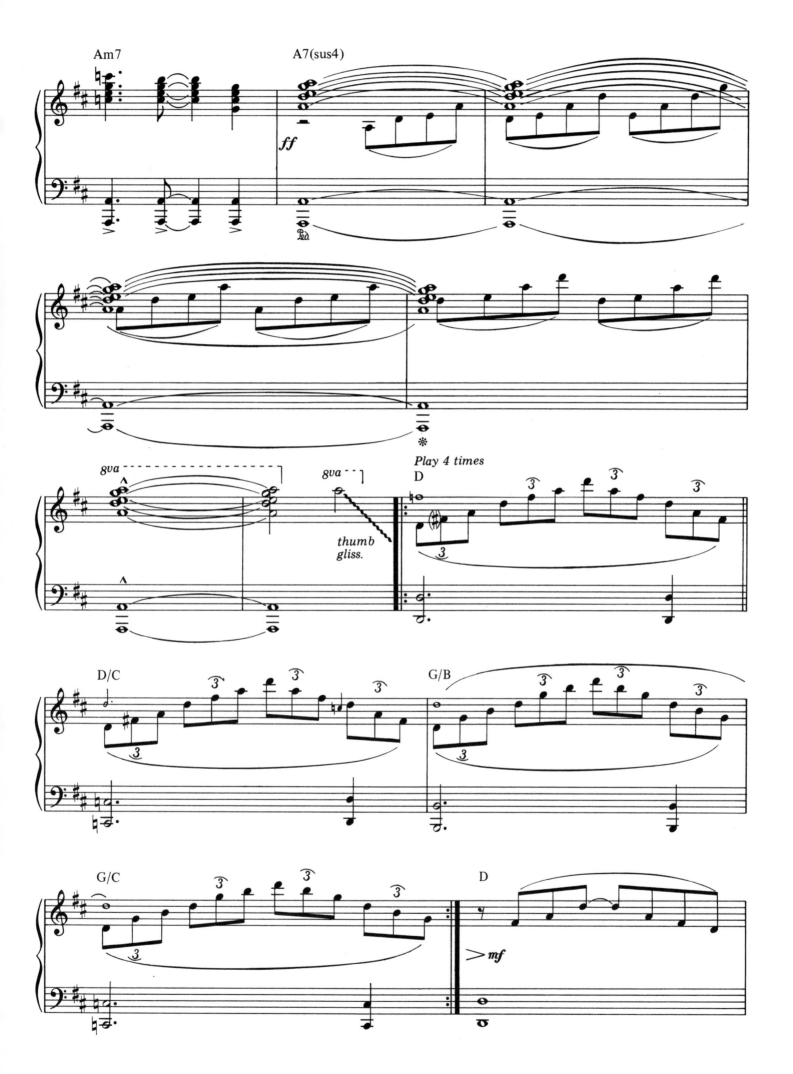

ELEANA

By Paul Senneville

ALL BY MYSELF

Words & Music by Eric Carmen

ALL I ASK OF YOU

Music by Andrew Lloyd Webber
Lyrics by Charles Hart

COLIN MAILLARD

By Paul de Senneville & Jean Baudlot

I DREAMED A DREAM
(From The Musical 'Les Miserables')

Music by Claude-Michel Schonberg   Lyric by Herbert Kretzmer
Original Text by Alain Boublil & Jean-Marc Natel